The Red-All-Over Riddle Book

George Szirtes

illustrated by Andrew Stooke

faber and faber
LONDON · BOSTON

First published in 1997
by Faber and Faber Limited
3 Queen Square London WC1N 3AU
This paperback edition first published in 1998

Typeset by Faber and Faber Ltd
Printed and bound in Great Britain by Mackays of Chatham plc,
Chatham, Kent

A CIP record for this book
is available from the British Library

ISBN 0-571-19224-6

10 9 8 7 6 5 4 3 2 1

for John Mole and John Cotton
who riddled before
and Jane Feaver
who suggested I should

DOOR
Bell

1 We push his nose when we want in
And he must squeal or chime or sing,
Like dentists we say, *Open wide!*
And once that's done we slip inside.

2 On the top sits fire,
In the middle gold
At the bottom grass.

At the top you stop
In the middle wait
And at the bottom, pass.

3 Fire in water
A delicate flick of flame

All glow, gape and gill,
Now darting, now still

The soul
Of the bowl

But leisurely, leisurely,
Sunken treasurely.

4 A tiny roar
at the tip of a stick,
one live shimmering feather,

then a luminous bird flapping scarlet wings
to the hot beat of its heart,

with feathers everywhere
crackling and cooing
fluttering, devouring,

the blackened bough it sits on.

5 Here come the angels
Like very loud tourists
Wielding their cameras
With built in flashes
Brightening dark weather.

6 Where am I? I do not know, I sit
Inside that girl. It's very dark. Between
My looking and her thinking is a space
For one whom neither she nor I have seen,
Who looks and thinks and in the darkness stirs
And dreams of us, or thinks the dream is hers.

7 Whoever invented it
must be turning in his grave

Whoever fitted it
must be rolling in it

Whoever thought of a square one
must be a strange felloe.

8 They tend to go round in circles
While coming straight to the point,
Have barely a leg to stand on
With only a single hip-joint

They pirouette, they twist around
With one black stump, one foot unshod
And leave small holes where they have trod.

9 His flat face may look like a light switch
and
his eyes like a pair of saucers
and
his beak like tiny tin-snips
and
his body like a soft pellet
but
to who?

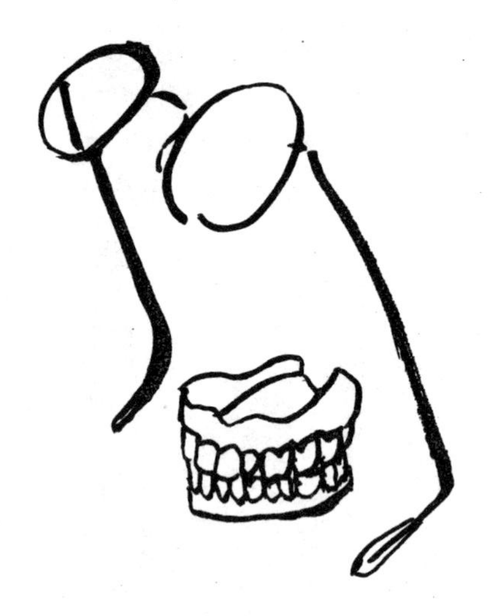

10 Firm in the saddle,
Riding the full force
Of the world as it strikes you,
They clear a way for you.

Later, in bed
They lie quietly,
Folding their arms and examining
Their own delicate wrists.

11 Two wheels rolled along
A man sat in the middle
Although he had no horse
He sat firm in the saddle
Although he had no car
He still pressed on the pedal
And so his feet went round
Both feet off the ground.

12 Time has handcuffed us:
Its small round face insists
We measure our own pulse
By glancing at our wrists.

13 All that breathing, heaving, running, steaming
All that mane and hoof and eye,
As if a simple block of wood were dreaming
And, in a vision, seemed to gallop by
While merely toing-and-froing,
Both standing still and going.

14 Squeaking not crowing
Never quite going
But pretty well knowing
Which way the wind's blowing.

15 I cling on in desperation
Grip the line and bob and pray
When wild storms rage through the garden
They won't blow your clothes away.
And now they're dry, do you intend
to keep me hanging on all day?

16 All too liable to snap
And light as a feather,
But willing to stretch the odd point
So when everything is threatening
To fall apart
It holds together.

17 They cover your ear
They cover your lip
They cram you with words
they give you the pip.

*

One chirrups on the table
Until you pick her up
And comfort her, poor thing,
But then you have to listen
To her endless nattering.

18 What makes him glow like that
Through his blood-red waistcoat
As if he had swallowed the sun
Or one small portion of it
To keep him going
All through winter?

19 I saw a bride splendid in white garments.
I saw a woman with one hundred children
The children plump and firm within her arms.
But some fell down or strangers took and ate them,
Cut them, sliced them, bit them, baked them,
  boiled them –
Alas, alas, a widow frail and naked
stood by my window in the heavy snow
Imagining, under the white snow, she was a bride
again.
In time, she sighed, in time.

20 To some a source of pride
To some a sheet of grief,
A kind of gaudy tie
Or giant handkerchief.

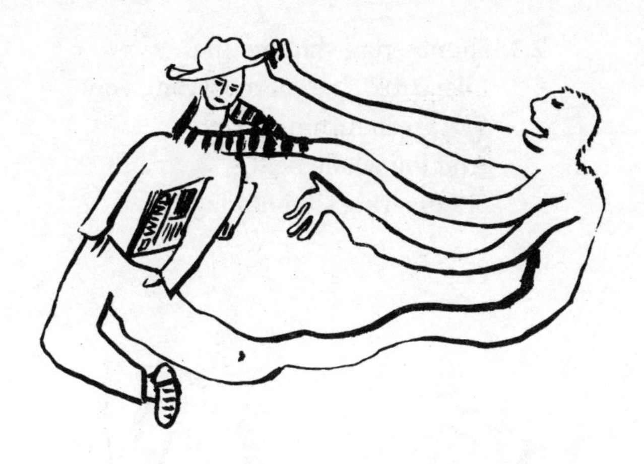

21 Light fingered, invisible
A thief through and through
He'll steal your hat, he'll whip your scarf
And your newspaper too.
He'll hang around street corners
And pounce as you go by
Or hover at your window
And slip in with a sigh.

22 Shimmering shimmering
Like stroking a cat the wrong way
The green turning silver
And the whole field
Shimmering shimmering.

23 So much water
The earth drinks down
You'd think poor little squiggly worms
Might well drown

And all the ants and beetles
And other creepy things
Rush round in a panic
Wearing water wings.

24 Above the green carpet
The great fried egg
Sits in his blue bath.

25 Ten moons, twenty moons,
Adult moons, baby moons,
Sharp little moons
Bent on fingers of cloud
Growing night and day

Then shorn away.

26 The first was the broadest
The second pointed the way
The third, the tallest, followed
The fourth one had the ring
The last, stuck on the end, was weakest.
Each found a key
all of them danced to music.
Who were they?

27 A tongue that never speaks,
A skin that's black or brown
going out for walks
But never on his own.

28 Tiny black beetles march in a line
But when you turn a new leaf over
Their spirits take wing
In your head.

29 Time is frozen in a box –
A flat tide in the dark –
The world resurfaces, a distant echo,
A stiff paper, bearing all our faces.

30 Look at him nibbling the page
Leaving the blue behind,
How efficient he must be,
So thin and straight and tall,
And always on the ball.

31 Here they come
Dancing on points
Doing the splits
Cold hearted dancers
With sharp cutting answers.

32 The more you hold him
The thinner he grows,
The wetter he gets
The brighter he glows,

The lither and leaner
The slimmer his shape,
The more likely he is
To want to escape.

The more he escapes
The more he grows leaner
Each time you touch him
You feel that much cleaner.

33 The dark queen's fingernail
A curving frosted smile
The face in the pail
An enchanted isle
pale silver bone
escaped balloon
or a coin thrown
one dull afternoon
into the sky and stuck
there by some piece of luck.

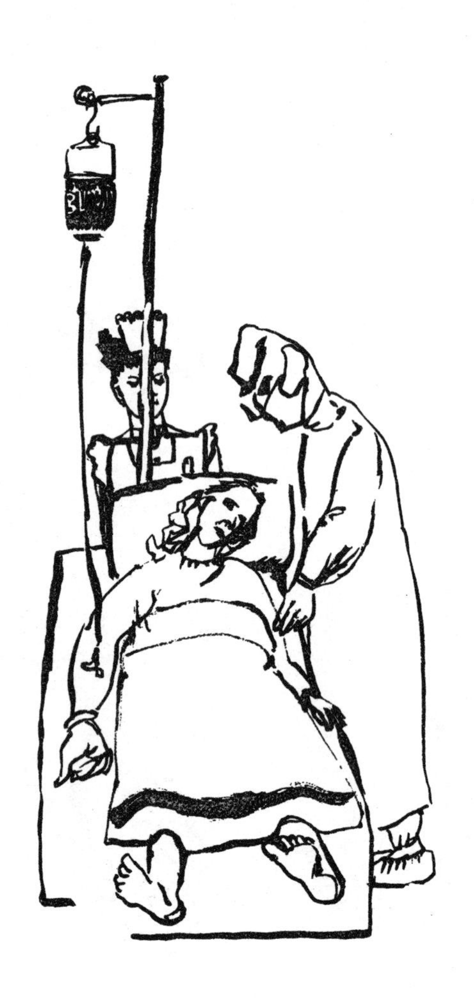

34 Red river through us,
Tributaries faintly
Marking out their courses,
Springing to the surface
At the tiniest pinprick
In terrifying beads
That briefly glow then harden
Crinkled as wee cowpats.

35 Look at the white cloth running on the wind.
Look at the pebble skimmed and swallowed,
The thousand curls and flecks that ride and fall,
The widening circles in the heart of the valley.

No one so clear as I am,
I who can show you your face
Or swallow you whole
Or sit quietly in the smallest container
Or run through a forest, laughing.

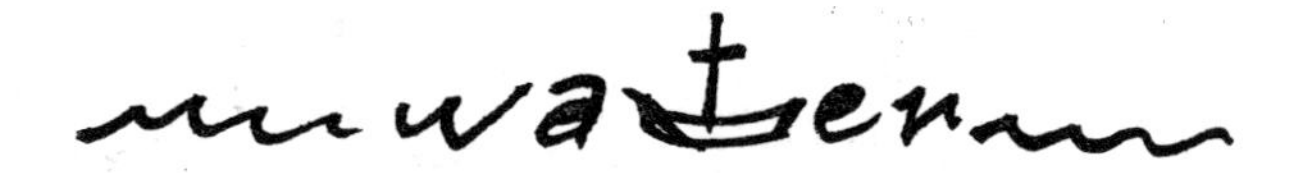

36 Behold the dual monarchy
Ruling over cutlery.
One's a scald
The other's cold,
But how the tears come pouring down
When you twist that fancy crown.

37 It has a head, it has a foot
Four other feet beside,
And then two extra human feet
Covered up inside,
And underneath that snow-white sheet
The small heart's reassuring beat.

38 Little boat, where is your mast?
You mean the leg? He's fast asleep
Where the waves of night time sweep
Across him. But I'm holding fast,
Yes, I'm anchored just off-shore
Safely on the bedroom floor.

39 Think of all those witches
Buried vertically
Only their hats showing.

Think of all those loudhailers
Whispering to tarmac
Making the whole road sing.

Think of all that red and white.
What a sight.
Mile after mile. Night after night.

40 Two armchairs, a settee,
Rolling down the road,
Behind a metal belly
Within which sparks explode

The furniture rolls on
The sparks explode in fumes,
Ten million mums and dads speed on
In small upholstered rooms.

41 A wrinkled paper bowl.
No fish swim in it,
No water fills it up,
But a hot sweltering
Unbearable lightness
Which comes on suddenly
As if some wonderful idea
Had struck fire in your bright head.

42 You fill my head with empty things
So when I get to speak
All I say is rubbish
And that but once a week.

43 I know a man – he lives in the wall,
He does his work by running about,
He runs up the ceiling – and there's light!
He runs into a box – and there is music!
He leaps across the street and our phone rings.
He runs about so much he gets quite hot.
Don't touch him or he'll kick you.

44 Hundreds of stiff white legs
On one enormous neck
And all those legs let loose
Inside your open mouth.

45 I saw a giraffe on the pavement
His eye was bright though he'd been turned
to stone
No feet, no belly, no tail, just one long neck
A dog sniffed at him but left him alone.

46 Grind grind
Crunch crunch
Get stuck in
It's time for lunch.

47 A long flat mouth for singing –
All those white teeth!
But the dentist never comes
To take out the black ones.

48 One hot belly
One big ear
One round lip
With two more near.

49 She took a black pencil,
Drew the eyes,
Shaded the cheekbones
Down to size,
Made sure each feature
Was properly defined,
Then took a piece of tissue paper
Dabbed her mouth

And left this soft red rose behind.

Solutions

1 Doorbell
2 Traffic Lights
3 Goldfish
4 Fire
5 Lightning
6 Russian Doll
7 Wheel
8 Compasses
9 Owl
10 Glasses
11 Bicycle
12 Watch
13 Rocking Horse
14 Weathercock
15 Clothes Peg
16 Rubber Band
17 Telephone Calls
18 Robin
19 Apple Tree
20 Flag
21 Wind
22 Wheat
23 Rain
24 Sun in the Sky
25 Fingernail
26 Fingers
27 Shoe
28 Print
29 Photograph
30 Ball Point Pen
31 Scissors
32 Soap
33 Moon
34 Blood

35 Water

36 Taps

37 Bed

38 Slipper

39 Traffic Cones

40 Cars

41 Paper Lamp Shade

42 Dustbin

43 Electricity

44 Toothbrush

45 Lamp Post

46 Teeth

47 Piano

48 Cup of Tea

49 Lipstick